Pirate School

Written by Lisa Thompson
Pictures by Craig Smith and Lew Keilar

A pirate's life is full of surprises. When Barnacle Bill came aboard, the crew of *The Black Beast* got a very nasty surprise. Barnacle Bill was the head of the Pirate School ship and he wasn't happy.

3

"Whirling whales!" said Barnacle Bill. "What kind of pirates are you? You have forgotten how to be bold, fierce and nasty. It's back to school for the lot of you!"

"Pirate School?" said Red Beard and his crew.

"Yes. Now get to your lessons," yelled Barnacle Bill.

The crew had lessons all day long at Pirate School. First on the timetable was sword-fighting.

Captain Red Beard cut his finger. He felt faint and his legs went wobbly.

"I think I need to go to sick bay," he wailed.

Barnacle Bill shook his head and raised his sword.

"What kind of pirates are you?" he cried.

Then there was cannon-firing class.

The Captain's red beard got burned when the cannon fired. Black soot covered the crew.

"Now you look like a crew of fierce pirates!" said Colin, the cannon master.

Barnacle Bill just shook his head.

"You may *look* like pirates, but you still have a lot to learn," he muttered.

9

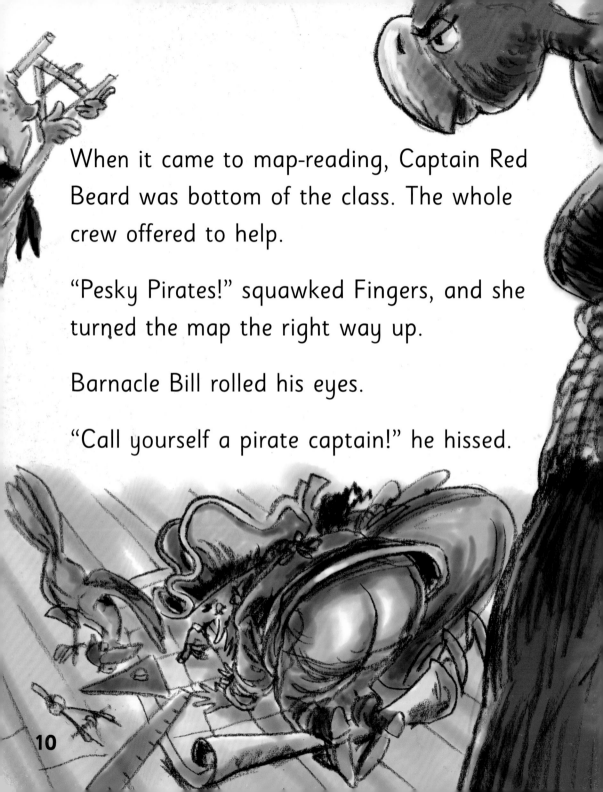

When it came to map-reading, Captain Red Beard was bottom of the class. The whole crew offered to help.

"Pesky Pirates!" squawked Fingers, and she turned the map the right way up.

Barnacle Bill rolled his eyes.

"Call yourself a pirate captain!" he hissed.

11

"Try using the compass," said Bones, the dog.

Lizzie pointed at the windvane. She told the Captain how it worked.

"How interesting," said Captain Red Beard.

Barnacle Bill gritted his teeth.

"I can't believe my ears!" he snarled. "Why not let Lizzie take your place? She knows far more about sailing than you do."

The next day, they had pirate band practice. The Captain and the crew were very bad.

The teachers hid in the sails and barrels to get away from the noise.

Captain Red Beard ordered his crew to play even louder. "Now this is music!" he said.

Barnacle Bill did not think so. He was having an afternoon nap. He stormed out onto the deck.

"What a dreadful din!" he yelled.

Treasure-sharing class was on Friday.
The crew were all happy to go to this class.

Captain Red Beard was not very good at adding or subtracting. His sharing skills were also very bad. His teacher almost walked the plank!

That night, Captain Red Beard and his crew remembered how to be pirates. They showed Barnacle Bill exactly what kind of pirates they were. Quickly and quietly, they set to work.

"Thanks for the treasure!" shouted Captain Red Beard.

"And the treasure map," cried Lizzie.

"You see, we are bold, fierce and clever pirates," shouted Captain Red Beard. "Maybe *you* still have a lot to learn!"

The crew all cheered as they sailed away.

21

"I think it's better to be a clever pirate than a nasty one," smiled Captain Red Beard. He jumped into his hammock and fell into a deep sleep.

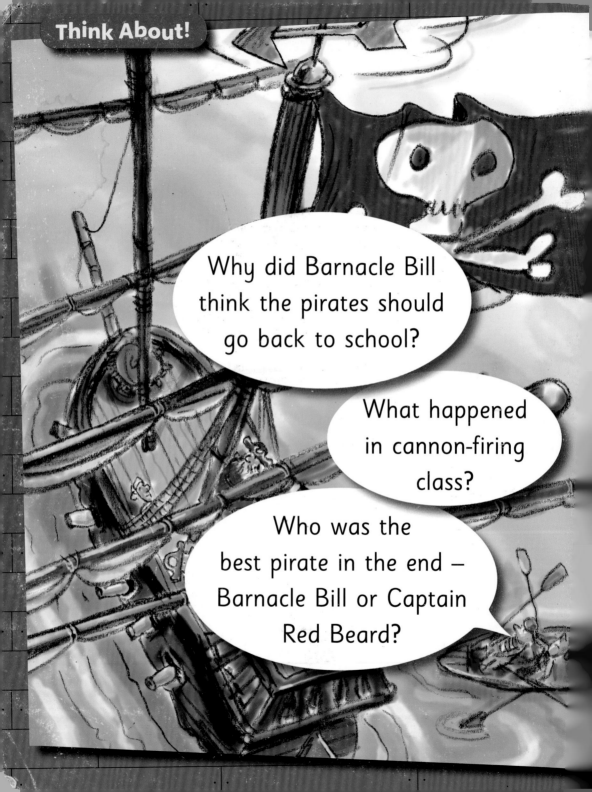